Fun Family Phonics

Written by Muriel Endersby (Naismith)
Illustrated by Elizabeth Hollick

With love to my family,
Rachel, Lydia, Debbie, and Esther,
their husbands, my grandchildren,
and Marina (Elizabeth's granddaughter)

Copyright © 1995 Muriel Endersby (Naismith). Reprinted in 2001.

Canadian Cataloguing in Publication Data

ISBN 0-9699735-0-0

Publisher Muriel Endersby

Printed in Canada by Thunderbird Press Ltd.

Muriel Endersby (Naismith)
White Rock, B.C.
Canada

About This Book

Teachers have successfully used the stories in this book as part of their reading program for more than thirty five years. Adults, who were once my students, tell me that they still have fond memories of;
                  "Apple on the tree"
                  "Bobby with his bag"
and all the other rhymes and stories that now comprise "Fun Family Phonics."

Letters are abstract symbols. Children have difficulty puzzling them out and distinguishing between them, as long as they remain abstract. This unique method of teaching phonics was invented to give life to these symbols and to provide a memory hook between the symbol and the sound that the letter makes in a word.

The stories center on the lower case letters because these are the ones that children find the most difficult. Capital letters are included in the text and each story begins with the capitalized form of the target letter.

Singing is fun for children and a wonderful teaching tool. The alphabet rhymes are all set to music with a catchy tune that children love to sing. Each verse includes the name, sound and shape of the letter. The action for each rhyme indicates how Dave discovered the sound of the letter. The action picture is at the bottom of the story page.

At home, children will benefit from hearing the stories and will easily learn to recognize the sounds and shapes of the phonetic alphabet, even if they have not met them in school.

Contents

Apple on the tree says **a a a**

Bobby with his **b**ag says **b b b**

Curly headed Colin says **c c c**

Drummer Dave says **d d d**

Egg in the cup says **e e e**

Fiona's funny feather says **f**

Gobbling goose says **g g g**

Hairy Humphrey says **h h h**

Ink on the desk says **I**

Jello in the jug says **j j j**

Kitchen chair breaking says **k**

Long legged Larry says **l l l**

Molly the milk cow says **m**

Nana in her nose says **n**

Oliver's olive says **o**

Popping popcorn says **p p p**

Quacking duck says **q q q**

Red rooster says **r r r**

Snake in the grass says **s s s**

Trickling tap says **t t t**

Uncle waking up says **u u u**

Violets in the vase say **v v v**

Water from the well says **w w w**

X-ray says **x x x**

Yolly's yacht says **y y y**

Zebra running zig zag says **z z z**

Meet The Fun Family

Do you know the Fun Family? Perhaps they live in your neighborhood. Mr. and Mrs. Fun have three children. Dave is not much older than you. He is a great detective. He listens for sounds and looks for shapes that give him clues about letters. Then he tells them to his sister, Jen, who is four. Their younger sister, Sue, is only two so she cannot understand the clues, but she likes to join in the fun.

Dave takes good care of his pet dog, a Dalmatian he calls Dot. Jen's pet is a frisky kitten she calls Kitty, and Sue has a cuddly teddy bear. Grandma and Granddad live close by and they often come to visit. The children call them Nana and Papa. Mrs. Fun's sister, Aunt Mary, lives in the old family farm house with her husband, Uncle Larry. The farm is an exciting place for the family to visit and a great place for Dave's detective work.

Dave has put all the letters he has discovered, while being a detective, into a big treasure box. Each story in this book will give you one "treasure" from this box. You'll enjoy finding them with Dave, and then you can play detective yourself and look for other things in the picture that begin with the same letter.

You will love singing the alphabet song. At the bottom of each story page you will see the action that you can do with each letter.

All these letters will help you learn to read, and that is the best fun of all!

Aa

Apple trees are good for climbing and Dave loves to climb.

At the top of the tree in the Fun family's back yard one last apple had attracted Dave's attention for a long time. Dave thought about **aiming** his bow and arrow at the apple, but he decided that this was not a good idea.

One afternoon he asked his mother if he could climb up and reach the apple. Dave climbed to the top of the tree with the arrows still attached to his back. Jen and Sue waited anxiously below. He held on tightly to a branch and reached out as far as he could. When he was about to touch the apple, the branch began to creak. It was then that detective Dave had an idea. Calling down to Jen, he said, "Look, Jen, the apple and the branch of the tree together make the letter 'a' and the creaking tree sounds like the letter 'a'."

"Apple on the tree says a a a."

(a is a vowel and sometimes says its name - **aiming**)

apple

apple

reaching apple

Bb

Bobby, the Letter Carrier passes by the Fun family's home every day, delivering mail to all the neighbors on the street.

One very hot afternoon, Jen and Dave had just come home from a birthday party and were playing in their back yard with their balloons and ball. They ran and stood beside the fence as Bobby passed by, but Bobby seemed too hot and tired to talk. His big bag had slipped down his back and was almost touching the ground. As he panted up the hill towards the bridge, he pressed his lips together and let out little puffs of air.

"I think Bobby has had a hard day," said Jen. "Maybe his big bag is full of birthday mail for our friend.

Just then detective Dave had an idea. "Bobby, with his big bag looks like the letter 'b'," said Dave, "and he is making the sound of the letter 'b' as he pants up the hill."

"Bobby with his bag says b b b."

big bag

big bag

holding bag

Cc

Colin Carter came to live in the house next door to the Fun family when he was only a few months old. Dave and Jen could hardly wait to go and see him. After they had called the Carter family to ask if they could visit, they bought a baby bib as a gift to carry with them. Mr. and Mrs. Carter and their daughter Cristy invited them to come into Colin's room. Colin was crying in his crib, but when he saw that he had company, he stopped crying and smiled while everyone crowded around his crib. Cristy showed Jen the clown she had bought for Colin and asked her if she would like to help her take Colin for a ride in his carriage. Jen thought Colin was very cute when he caught hold of her finger and tried to talk to her. Of course babies can't really talk, but they can make noises and copy sounds that they hear.

Detective Dave was listening and watching. "Colin is saying the first sound of his name," exclaimed Dave. "It is the sound of the letter 'c' and look, each of his curls looks like the letter 'c'."

"Curly-headed Colin says c c c."

curly

curly

touching neck

Dd

Dave loves to play **d**rums. He thinks he would like to be a **d**rummer when he is older and play in the marching band with his uncle. Uncle Larry lets **D**ave practice on his big base **d**rum. It is too big to hang **d**own from his waist, so he puts it on the floor in front of his feet.

Dave's **D**almatian **d**og named **D**ot also enjoys the **d**rum. **D**o you know what **D**ot **d**oes when **D**ave is playing? He **d**ances! Aunt Mary calls him "**D**ot, the **d**ancing **d**og." Aunt Mary has a violin and sometimes she and **D**ave play a **d**uet. That makes **D**ot **d**o a **d**ifferent kind of **d**ance.

One **d**ay when **D**ave was **d**rumming and **D**ot was **d**ancing, **d**etective **D**ave noticed his reflection in the mirror and was **d**elighted to **d**iscover that he and the **d**rum together made the shape of the letter "**d**". When he beat the **d**rum it sounded like the letter "**d**".

"**D**rummer **D**ave says **d d d.**"

drummer

drummer

beating **d**rum

Ee

Everyone in the Fun family **en**joys **e**ggs for breakfast. They **e**specially like the **e**xtra large **e**ggs that come from Uncle Larry's farm.

Dave often puts his **e**gg in a little cup to **eat** it. When he has finished **eating,** he turns the shell upside down and tricks his dad. **E**veryone laughs when dad cuts the **e**mpty **e**gg.

One morning mother had left a <u>raw</u> **e**gg in a little cup on the table. When dad **e**ntered the kitchen, he **e**xclaimed, "You can't fool me with that **e**gg shell, Dave." Quickly he took a knife to cut the **e**gg, but he missed and cut the cup! The **e**gg spilled out over the table! Jen cried "**e**" when she saw the yucky mess. Father said, "This time, you have fooled me!" Dave gazed at the **e**gg with his detective **e**yes. "Look," he **e**xclaimed, "the broken **e**gg looks like the letter '**e**' and Jen made the sound of the letter '**e**' when she saw the mess."

"**E**gg in the cup says **e**."

("**e**" is a vowel and sometimes says its name - **eating**)

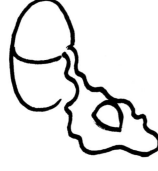 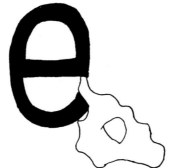

egg   egg   expressing disgust

Ff

Fancy hats are one of Jen's favorite dress-up clothes. Aunt Fiona frequently gives Jen the old fashioned hats that she no longer wears. Jen's favorite fancy hat is a furry one with a long fluffy feather.

One day mother was in a hurry to go to the grocery store, but first she wanted the children to put the toys away. In his efforts to finish the clean-up job, Dave forced Aunt Fiona's hat into the toy box. "Crack" went the feather. Poor Jen felt sad and a little angry, because she was really fond of the feather. Dave was sorry about the accident and fetched a band aid to fix it. Every one laughed when they saw the funny-looking feather. Then detective Dave had an idea. He said to Jen, "Now the feather that Aunt Fiona gave you looks like the letter 'f', and when you say the sound of the letter 'f', you can feel the air blowing as softly as a feather."

"Fiona's funny feather says f."

feather

feather

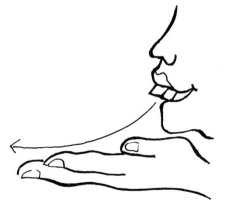

blowing through teeth over lower lip

Gg

Geese can get very grumpy. One day when Dave and Jen wanted to find Gertie the goose, who lives on the farm, Uncle Larry suggested that they go and look in the leaves behind the barn. Aunt Mary gave Jen some green grapes to give to the goose. Grandma and Grandpa had just arrived at the farm gate. The goat was already there to greet them.

Gertie, the goose, was feeling very grumpy. She was almost buried in a great pile of leaves and did not want to be disturbed. Jen tried to give her the bunch of green grapes, but she just twisted her head towards them and gobbled grumpily, as if to say, "Go away!" Jen was a little disappointed that Gertie did not want the grapes and was not going to come out of the leaves.

Just as they were about to go, detective Dave gazed at Gertie. "Her head and neck look like the letter 'g'," said Dave, "and when she gobbles she sounds like the letter 'g'."

"Gobbling goose says g g g."

goose

goose

pushing away

Hh

Hairy Humphrey, Henry's dog, lives just up the hill from the Fun family's home. Dave's dog, Dot, enjoys playing and racing with Humphrey. When Humphrey runs fast, he gets very hot because his hair is so thick. He also breathes heavily and arches his back.

One hot day Dave and Henry decide to race with their dogs down the hill to Dave's house. Mother was outside holding the hose. The dogs ran into the back yard with Dave and Henry close behind them. While Humphrey stood panting with his back arched and his tail in the air, Dave and Henry hurried into the house to get the dogs some water. Mother helped Humphrey cool down by spraying him with her hose.

When Dave and Henry came out of the house with the water and headed for the dogs, Dave's detective eyes notice something interesting about Humphrey. He said, "When Humphrey puts his tail in the air and arches his back he looks like the letter 'h', and can you hear how his panting sounds like the letter 'h'?"

"Hairy Humphrey says h h h."

hairy

hairy

breathing "h"

Ii

It is a rule in the Fun family that nobody plays in Dad's office. One **icy** cold day, when there was nothing very interesting to do, the children decided to play hide and go seek. Jen closed her eyes and counted while Sue climbed inside the toy box. Dave went into his dad's office with Dot, his impish dog, close behind him. Dave watched Jen pass the door of the office and then made a dash to get "home free". Immediately, Dot leaped over the desk to follow Dave. Unfortunately he knocked over an ink bottle making two inky blobs on Dad's desk. Dave rushed into the kitchen to find something to clean up the ink. Just then Dad walked into his office! Seeing the ink blobs on his desk, he exclaimed "i". Dave knew he was in trouble and said he was sorry. As they worked together to clean up the mess, detective Dave noticed something interesting. "The spilt ink looks like the letter 'i'," he said, "and Dad made the sound of the letter 'i' when he saw the inky mess."

"Ink on the desk says **i**."

(**i** is a vowel and sometimes says its name - "**icy**")

ink	ink	pointing to ink

Jj

Jen and Dave just love jello. Making jello for lunch is a job they both enjoy. One morning Jen put jello powder into a jug and stirred in hot water. Dave added icy cold orange juice to make the jello even more juicy. Just then, Mrs. Jones phoned. Her little boy had jabbed his finger with a fork and her baby was also crying. Mom took Sue with her and went to help Mrs. Jones. She told the children not to touch the jello while she was gone.

Jen played with her Jack-in-the-box and Dave looked at his Jungle book for a while, but mother was gone a long time. Dave could not wait and he reached for the ladle that was still in the jug of jello. He heard a jiggling sound as he lifted it because the jello was almost set. At that moment Jen noticed mother coming home. Dave jumped as he heard the door.   "I was just testing it Mom", he said.

Detective Dave had seen some clues. Lifting the ladle again, he said to Jen, "This looks like the shape of the letter 'j', and when I raise the ladle, the jello jiggles and sounds like the letter 'j'."

"Jello in the jug says j j j."

jello

jello

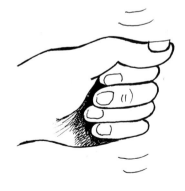

lifting ladle

Kk

   Kitchen chairs in the Fun family are getting old and fragile.

   "No running in the house" is a Fun family rule, but sometimes Dave and Jen forget. One day Dave was trying out his **k**ite in the house, and he grabbed Jen's doll to tease her. He ran through the **k**itchen, the dining room, the living room, and back into the **k**itchen, with Jen close behind him. **K**itty, Jen's little **k**itten, hid under a **k**itchen chair to **k**eep out of the way.   Dave raced into the **k**itchen for the third time. As he was looking behind him, he **k**icked into the **k**itchen chair where Jen's **k**itten was hiding. Out dashed the **k**itten. "Crash" went the chair. Up went the seat as one front leg snapped, and it fell to the back of the chair. Mom ran in when she heard the noise. Dave knew that he should not have been running and said he was sorry and would pay for the chair to be fixed. He looked again at the broken chair and said to Jen, "The **k**itchen chair now looks like a '**k**', and the noise it made when it broke was the sound of the letter '**k**'."

"**K**itchen chair breaking says **k**."

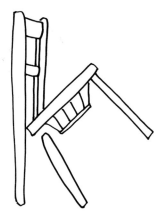

kitchen

kitchen

showing break

Ll

Life on a farm is always busy. Uncle Larry must look after his farm in all kinds of weather.

One stormy day when Dave and Jen were visiting the farm, Uncle Larry put on his long-legged boots and started out across the back lawn. Dave and Jen longed to go with him, but they had left their boots at home. For a long time they looked through the screen door, watching the lightening and listening to the loud thunder. At last the rain stopped and the sun peeped out. Dave noticed a ladder leaning against a tree near the house. Quickly they climbed a little way up the ladder and listened for Uncle Larry. It was not long before they heard a sound that made them laugh. Uncle Larry came around the corner, carrying a letter, and they noticed that his long boots were making a funny noise as he lifted each one from the mud. "Listen Jen," said detective Dave, "Uncle Larry is making the sound of the letter 'l', and his long body and legs look like the letter 'l'."

"Long-legged Larry says l l l."

long legs

long legs

lifting feet

Mm

Most of the cows on Uncle Larry's farm are milked by machine. The cows must be milked early in the morning before the milk truck arrives.

Molly is more nervous than the other cows and does not like the milking machine, so Aunt Mary makes Molly happy by milking her by hand. One morning mother and the children met with Mary in the barn to watch the milking. Molly did not mind when they each took a turn to do the milking. When Jen tried to make the milk go in the pail, she missed and had to mop it up! Molly was very contented when Mary was milking her, and she quietly "mooed" as if to say "thank you very much." Detective Dave listened to Molly, then, looking at her face, he said, "Molly's nose looks like the letter 'm', and she is making the sound of the letter 'm'."

"Molly the milk cow says m."

milk   milk   pressing finger on lip

Nn

     Nana and Papa were staying over **n**ight with the their grandchildren. Just before bed time Sue climbed on **N**ana's lap, wearing her **n**ew **n**ightie, while Papa sat reading the **n**ewspaper. "Watch out for my knitting **n**eedles!" said **N**ana. Sue held on to the **n**eedles and touched **N**ana's **n**ice red **n**ecklace. Then she reached up for **N**ana's glasses. **N**ana said, "**N**o Sue, you should **n**ever pull on glasses because they break easily. Without glasses I would **n**ot be able to see very well!" Then **N**ana said, "I can show you a **n**ifty **n**ose trick. When I make a special sound, it makes my **n**ose buzz. Put your finger on my **n**ose and feel."

     Detective Dave **n**oticed what Sue was doing and said, "**N**ana's **n**ose looks like the letter '**n**', and when she makes Sue's finger tingle, she is making the sound of the letter '**n**'."

"**N**ana in her **n**ose says **n**"

Now, you try that **n**ifty **n**ose trick!

nose

nose

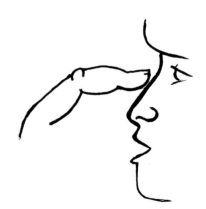

touching nose

Oo

On Friday evening Mr. and Mrs. Fun invited some **of** their friends to their house for supper. Dave was allowed to stay up and welcome the guests, but he was not to eat the food. Each friend brought part of the supper. Dave felt hungry when he saw the **o**melets, **o**ranges, **oval** cake and even an **o**ctopus. Then, **O**liver arrived with a jar **of** green **o**bjects which Dave thought must be grapes. He handed the jar to Dave. In the kitchen, when nobody was looking, Dave took **o**ff the lid and popped one into his mouth. What a surprise he had! "**O o o**," he cried, as he pulled out the **o**live, "this is not a grape!" Dave had learned his lesson.

Dave thought about his mistake in bed that night. He also remembered the sound he had made when he tasted the **o**live. Suddenly he discovered a clue. The **o**live was shaped like the letter '**o**', and the noise he had made was the sound of the letter '**o**'.

"**O**liver's **o**live says **o o o**."

(**o** is a vowel and sometimes says its name - **oval**)

olive

olive

forming "O"

Pp

Papa gave a **p**opcorn **p**opper to the family as a **p**resent. Sue thought it was a **p**arty every time they used it. One day when Dad had **p**lugged in the **p**opper and **p**ut corn in the top, the front door bell rang and everyone ran to meet Nana and **P**apa. Dad had forgotten to **p**ut the **p**ail under the **p**opper, and when they returned to the kitchen, **p**opcorn was **p**opping all over the **p**lace. The children joined in the fun by **p**retending to **p**op like the corn. Jen's **p**et kitten joined in the fun. She **p**ounced on the **p**opcorn and then **p**layed with the **p**ieces. The children didn't want their **p**arents to **p**ut the **p**ail under the **p**opcorn machine because they were having so much fun. Suddenly Dave stopped jumping. He had been using his detective eyes and ears. "The **p**opping **p**opcorn sounds like the letter '**p**'," he said, "and the **p**opper looks like the letter '**p**'."

"**P**opping **p**opcorn says **p p p**."

popcorn

popcorn

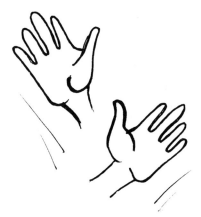

shooting upwards

Quite a variety of animals are born each year on Uncle Larry's farm. One quiet spring morning the ducklings hatched. What excitement there was in the Fun family as they planned a quick visit to the farm! Aunt Mary was at the gate to greet them, and together they hurried to the pond. "Go quietly," warned Aunt Mary, "the ducks might be quite scared." After the children had fed them lettuce, they each held a soft fluffy duckling. Sue just loved her duckling and wanted to take it home, but Mother duck started quacking. "You see," said Dave, "the duckling belongs with its family." Poor Sue just didn't understand and she started crying. "I have a plan," said Dave, "if you put the duckling back and quit crying, I'll buy you something special after we get home." Well, that stopped the tears, and Sue gave back her duckling.

Dave bought Sue a little toy duck. It cost him all of the quarters in his piggy bank. As Sue pulled it along, the head moved and it made a sound like a duck quacking. Dave suddenly had an idea. "That duck looks like the letter `q' and it makes the sound of the the letter `q'," he said.

"Quacking duck says q q q."

quacking

quacking

moving head while quacking

Rr

   Red **r**ooster **r**ules the farm yard. Each morning he **r**ouses everyone with his proud crowing. One morning **r**ed **r**ooster was not crowing with his **r**egular sound. Uncle Larry knew that he was in trouble and needed **r**escuing. It was **r**aining when Dave and Uncle Larry **r**eached the barnyard. The **r**ooster was on the **r**oof and seemed **r**eally scared. Uncle Larry **r**ested the ladder against the **r**oof and climbed up with Dave close behind. **R**ight away Uncle Larry knew why the **r**ooster was worried. A baby **r**accoon was also on the **r**oof sniffing the **r**ambler **r**oses! Uncle Larry **r**eached out his hand to **r**escue the **r**ooster, but then, he **r**ealized that one of the **r**ooster's feet was caught in a **r**ing attached to the **r**oof. Carefully he unhooked the **r**ing and freed the **r**ooster. As he did so, Dave looked at the **r**ooster's head. It was shaped like the letter '**r**'!

   Back in the farm house Dave **r**an to find Jen. He told her that the **r**ooster sounded like the letter '**r**' when he was scared and his head looked like the letter '**r**'.

"**R**ed **r**ooster says **r r r**."

rooster

rooster

pulling on
trapped leg

Ss

Sometimes Dave and Jen search for surprises by the stream on Uncle Larry's farm. One day, as they were strolling beside the stream, they saw a squirrel scampering in the trees, a spider building a spectacular web, and a small snail making a slimy trail beside the stream. Suddenly Dave stopped. There in the grass was a slippery snake. Jen, who had just seen the snake, squealed with surprise and then slapped her hands over her mouth. Unfortunately, it was too late. The snake had heard them and quickly slithered down a nearby hole to his secret underground home. Dave was a little sad to see the snake go. Then he started to think about what he had seen and heard. He said to Jen, "Did you hear the sound that the snake made as it slithered away?" It was the sound of the letter 's', and the snake looked like the letter 's'."

"Snake in the grass says s."

snake

snake

slithering like
snake

Tt

Taking a bath is a special treat in Uncle Larry's old farm house because the tub, toilet, and taps are all old fashioned, like the rest of the house.

One night, as Dave and Jen tried to go to sleep, Dave heard a "t t t" sound. Was it the clock ticking or a woodpecker tapping? It seemed to be coming from the bathroom. Jen said, "It must be a tap that has not been turned off." Dave felt he was too tired to get up, but then he imagined what might happen if the water overflowed onto the floor. He had also forgotten to brush his teeth. For two minutes Dave lay in bed trying to decide what to do. Then, he tiptoed into the bathroom carrying his toy tiger and took his toothpaste off the sink. He was just about to take his toothbrush and clean his teeth, when his detective eyes noticed that the tap was shaped like the letter 't', and the water trickling from the tap sounded like the letter 't'. Quickly, he cleaned his teeth, turned off the tap, and ran into the bedroom to tell Jen, who was still awake, about his terrific discovery.

* "Trickling tap says t t t."

* You may call this tap a faucet. In the old farm house it is called a tap

tap

tap

demonstrating
tap trickling

Uu

Uncle Larry gets **up** at six o'clock every morning to milk the cows. One day, when Dave and Jen were staying at the farm house, Dave did not get **up** at his **usual** time because he wanted to help **U**ncle Larry with the cows. At six o'clock Dave was already **up** and dressed. He hurried into **U**ncle Larry's room where he was surprised to see his dog **u**nderneath the bed, sleeping on an **u**mbrella! Poor **U**ncle Larry was feeling **u**nusually sleepy. Dave **u**ncovered his toes and showing him the clock, said, "The cows will not be milked **u**nless you get **up**. It's six o'clock!" "**U**nfortunately you are right!" said **U**ncle Larry as he stretched his arms above his head and yawned. "**U**ncle Larry," cried Dave, "you are making the letter **u** with your arms, and when you yawned you sounded like the letter '**u**'."

"**U**ncle waking **up** says **u u u**."

(**u** is a vowel and sometimes says its name - **usual**)

uncle   uncle   raising arms

Vv

Violets are Aunt Mary's favorite flowers. One morning Dave and Jen went looking for **v**iolets beside the stream where they had seen the snake in the grass. A **v**ariety of beautiful wild flowers grew there. Dave and Jen picked just a few **v**iolets with long stems and took them back to the farmhouse.

Aunt Mary had already been to the garden and picked **v**egetables for lunch and she had even tried to practice her **v**iolin. Dave helped Aunt Mary find a **v**ery special **v**ase that was just right for **v**iolets. Just then, Nana and Papa arrived. They always enjoyed **v**isiting their family on the farm.

While Dave was arranging the flowers, Jen took one **v**iolet from the **v**ase and rubbed it on her lower lip. "It feels so **v**elvety," she said. "It even makes my lip tingle." That gave detective Dave a clue. "The feel of the **v**iolet is just like the feeling you get on your lips when you make the sound of the letter '**v**'," said Dave, "and the **v**ase looks like the letter '**v**'."

"Violets in the **v**ase say **v v v**."

vase

vase

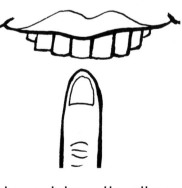
touching tingling
lower lip

Ww

When Dave visits Uncle Larry's farm, he often wonders about the way the farm used to be when his Great Grandfather lived there. One day he wanted to know where the family used to get their water, because he had heard that there were no taps in the house when it was first built. Uncle Larry explained that the water came from a well, which was still on the farm. Together with Jen they walked to the well with a pail. An old wagon wheel was resting on the well wall. Of course Dave wanted to get water from the well, so while Jen and Uncle Larry watched and waited, Dave lowered the pail into the well. What a long way down it went! At last it hit the water and the pail filled. Then Dave turned the handle and wound the pail up to the top of the well wall. The wind was blowing so hard that the water in the pail was whipped into waves which splashed against the side of the pail. "Look at the 'w' shape the waves are making," cried Dave, "and the water sounds like the letter 'w' as it hits the side of the pail."

"Water from the well says w w w."

water

water

tracing wave

Xx

X-rays don't hurt at all. Dave and Jen know that, but Sue is too young to understand.

Sue tries to copy the things that Dave and Jen do. One day she was climbing in the apple tree and she slipped and fell to the ground on her arms. She was crying as mother drove her to the hospital for **X**-rays. It took quite a time to persuade her to place her arms under the **X**-ray machine because she was scared it would hurt. When she finally agreed, she crossed her arms, and heard a little sound. Mother said, "The **X**-ray has been taken and it didn't hurt at all, did it?"

Back in the waiting area Sue told Jen and Dave about the sound that the machine had made. Together with the doctor they looked at the **X**-ray pictures on a screen. Fortunately, nothing was broken! This time Jen was the detective. "Look Sue," she said, pointing to the screen, "Your **X**-ray is shaped like the letter '**x**', and the noise you heard when the **X**-ray was taken, was the sound of the letter '**x**'."

"**X**-ray says **x**."

x-ray

x-ray

crossing arms

Yy

Yolly is a friend who has a sailboat. which he calls his **y**acht. One day , when Dave and Jen had walked along the beach to talk to him, **Y**olly said, "if **y**ou ask **y**our parents, **y**ou can come for a sail with me." "**Y**ippee," **y**elled Dave, and raced down the beach with Jen close behind him. "**Y**ou will need life jackets," said Dad. "Does **Y**olly have life jackets for **y**ou?" "Oh **y**es," replied Dave, "they are red, not **y**ellow like ours at home." They all walked back to **Y**olly's **y**acht. Sue wanted to go too, but Mom said that she was too **y**oung. Mom gave **y**ogurt to everyone for a snack, and Jen took her **y**oyo to play with on the **y**acht.

It was fun sailing! **Y**olly leaned back and **y**awned. Suddenly a big speedboat passed quite close to **Y**olly's **y**acht causing waves to tilt the boat. The mast holding the sail began to creak. Dave grabbed the ropes that held the sail . It was then that his detective eyes noticed the shape of the mast and sail. "They look like the letter '**y**'," he told Jen, "and the creaking mast sounds like the letter '**y**'."

"**Y**olly's **y**acht says **y y y**."

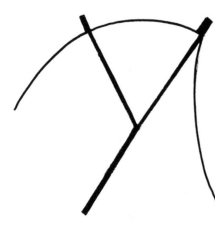

yacht

yacht

demonstrating
creaking mast

Zz

Zebras have their homes in faraway countries, but maybe you have seen one at the **z**oo. This last story is about a **z**ebra at the **z**oo.

For a special outing the Fun family planned a trip with friends and relations to visit the **z**oo. Sue was very excited because she had never been there. She put on the new dress with the **z**ipper in the front and could hardly wait until it was time to go.

Every cage at the **z**oo was so interesting! Sue wanted to see everything. She ran ahead to another cage. "Look Mom," she called, "Here is a horse with black and white stripes." Everyone laughed as they crowded round the cage. Suddenly the **z**ebra started to run back and forth looking quite upset. Then Dad noticed a bee was buzzing by the **z**ebra's nose. The **z**ebra's tail could not reach it. The crowd watched unable to help the poor **z**ebra. At last the bee left and flew away. Everyone clapped. Detective Dave had been watching and listening. "The buzzing bee sounded like the letter '**z**'," Dave told Jen, "and his **z**ig **z**ag running looked like the letter '**z**'."

"**Z**ebra running **z**ig **z**ag says **z z z**."

zig zag

zig zag

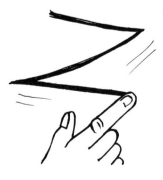

tracing zig zag

As a University College instructor, I have observed declining reading and writing skills in recent successive freshman classes. As a parent, I have a nine year old in the K-12 system receiving help from a five year old in Muriel Naismith's reading programme. Need I say more?

David J. Sale Dip. Tech., M.B.A., C.G.A.
KWANTLEN UNIVERSITY COLLEGE

Remembering how thrilled my children were as they mastered the alphabet in Muriel's preschool, I was excited about trying her methods with my Kindergarten classes.

Her approach captures my students' interest, and gives them a strong basis for learning beginning reading skills.

Victoria Jones   Surrey Centre Elem.

The first time I saw this program delivered to my daughter I knew it had untapped potential. The beauty and simplicity of this approach to phonics is at last being shared. It will undoubtably become a valued educational tool.

Carol Trauman
High School Teacher

We have been using this phonic program in our preschools for the last seven years and have found it to be extremely successful. Parents frequently tell us about the ease with which their children learned to read because of the excellent preparation they had in preschool.

Rachel Cram B.Ed., E.C.E.
Wind and Tide Preschool